YOU ARE THE

WEAKEST LINK

GOODBYE!

PUFFIN BOOKS

PUFFIN BOOKS

Published by the Penguin Group
Penguin Books Ltd, 27 Wrights Lane, London W8 5TZ, England
Penguin Putnam Inc., 375 Hudson Street, New York, New York 10014, USA
Penguin Books Australia Ltd, Ringwood, Victoria, Australia
Penguin Books Canada Ltd, 10 Alcorn Avenue, Toronto,
Ontario, Canada M4V 3B2
Penguin Books India (P) Ltd, 11 Community Centre, Panchsheel Park,
New Delhi – 110 017, India
Penguin Books (NZ) Ltd, Cnr Rosedale and Airborne Roads,
Albany, Auckland, New Zealand
Penguin Books (South Africa) (Pty) Ltd, 5 Watkins Street, Denver Ext 4,
Johannesburg 2094, South Africa

On the World Wide Web at: www.penguin.com

Penguin Books Ltd, Registered Offices: Harmondsworth, Middlesex, England

First published 2001

1

By arrangement with the BBC
The BBC logo and Weakest Link logo are trademarks of the
British Broadcasting Corporation and are used under licence.

BBC logo © BBC 1996
Weakest Link logo © BBC 2000

Additional material written by Rod Green

Designed and typeset by seagulls

Set in Gill Sans Educational

Made and printed in England by Clays Ltd, St Ives plc

British Library Cataloguing in Publication Data
A CIP catalogue record for this book is available from the British Library

ISBN 0–141–31363–3

YOU ARE THE WEAKEST LINK ... GOODBYE!

Welcome to the Weakest Link quiz book.

Some of you, of course, won't be with us for long. Some of you just won't be able to handle the pace. There's no room for bumblers or ditherers in this game. If you think the TV show is tough, then this quiz book is going to feel like climbing a glass mountain in treacle-soled shoes while it's raining banana skins – the only way is down.

The questions will come thick and fast. Your job is to be fast and not thick. Think you can hack it? Let's see if you still feel so confident when all your mates are watching you struggling to remember the longest river in France or how many degrees there are in a circle. You might think those questions are easy – but they won't all seem that way, especially when the pressure is on.

With this quiz book any number of players can take part. The main aim is simple – bin the birdbrains, dump the dopes and kick out the knuckleheads until there are just two of you slugging it out in the Head-to-Head.

Each round is played against the clock and at the end of the round everyone votes for one player to be dropped from the game. That player has to take the Walk of Shame and hear the dreaded words 'You are the weakest link ... Goodbye!'

Will you be the first to be voted off? If not, how long will you last? Are you smart enough to stay in the game right to the end, or will you cave in at a critical moment?

It's time to find out. Let's play the Weakest Link.

HOW TO PLAY THE WEAKEST LINK

HOW MANY PLAYERS?

One to three players

You can use this book on your own as a straightforward general knowledge quiz book, just working to build up your own highest score.

With two players you can take turns to ask each other questions to see who gets the highest score. If you have three players, one of you can be the quizmaster posing questions to the other two, and giving them a hard time when they slip up.

Four to ten players

Once you have four or more players, the real fun begins because you can elect a quizmaster and you will have to vote off the weakest link at the end of each round. If you have ten players – one quizmaster and nine contestants – you can copy the TV show and work through all the rounds. If there are four of you, after the first round you'll immediately be left with two contestants and have to go straight into the Head-to-Head. It will be a short but very exciting game!

More than ten players

In this case you will have to chose a quizmaster and then split up into teams, with one whole team being voted off at the end of each round.

HOW TO PLAY THE WEAKEST LINK

THE BASIC RULES

◯ First you must elect a quizmaster. Each player writes the name of the person you think would make the best quizmaster on a piece of paper. Voting for yourself is not allowed! Once everyone is ready, reveal the names on the papers. The person with the most votes becomes quizmaster. In the case of a tie, you must choose between those with equal votes by voting again.

◯ The game starts with Round One, which lasts three minutes. The rounds get shorter by ten seconds each time. If you don't have a clock or a watch with a second hand to time the rounds, then decide at the beginning how many questions each contestant must answer. We suggest each contestant answers at least three questions per round.

◯ Start each round with the player whose name comes first alphabetically. The quizmaster will ask as many questions as they can (and let you know whether you got the answer right of wrong) in the time given for that round.

◯ At the end of each round, the contestants must vote for who they think was the weakest link.

◯ To vote, each competitor writes down the name of the person they think is the weakest link. Make your vote without any discussion and don't let anyone see the name you're writing. The quizmaster will then ask the contestants, working from left to right, to reveal the name they have written. The player with the most votes hears the dreaded words 'You are the weakest link … Goodbye!'

◯ If two or more players have an equal number of votes, the players not involved in the tie must vote again – as many times as is necessary – until the weakest link has been determined.

○ Once you are down to just two contestants, regardless of which round you are on, those two go straight to Round Nine, the Head-to-Head. There they answer up to five questions each. The one who gets most right is the overall winner.

○ If there is a tie after Round Nine, the two players go into the Sudden Death round. Each player is asked an equal number of questions, answering in turn. The player who gets a question wrong and allows their opponent to go ahead by one correct answer loses!

THE OPTIONAL RULES

The fun part of this game is always going to be weeding out the weakest link – and avoiding becoming one yourself! But there are a couple of ways you can spice things up even more. These optional rules allow you to work as a team to keep a score and to keep tabs on just who is the weakest and strongest link. Using these options will keep the quizmaster very busy and so they may want to choose an assistant to help them keep track of everything – maybe the first of the weakest links dropped from the game.

Tracking the Weakest Link

○ If the quizmaster wants to know exactly who is letting the team down they can keep a record of whether each player is answering questions correctly or incorrectly. Write the initials of all the contestants on a piece of paper and put a tick against the initials of a contestant who answers a question correctly, a cross when they get one wrong.

○ At the end of each round, after the weakest link is voted off, the quizmaster can use these notes to let everyone know who really did mess up their answers and who is storming ahead.

Scoring and Banking Points

○ If you decide you want to play for points, you'll have to work together as a team. Each contestant will score one point for every question answered correctly. Keep a record of the score at the end of each round. The aim is to build up as high a score as possible. But don't be surprised if you find it difficult to build up those points. The questions are random and everyone may end up with their 'dreaded' subject!

○ The other great thing about building up a score is running the risk of losing the lot! If anyone gets a question wrong, all the points from that round are lost and you start the round again with zero. Getting an answer wrong when a lot of points depend on it will almost definitely make you the weakest link!

○ When only two players are remaining they move on to Round Eight, where they have a last opportunity to increase their score. At the end of Round Eight add up all the end of round scores – this is the total score with which the players enter the Head-to-Head.

○ You don't lose points for getting a wrong answer in the Head-to-Head or the Sudden Death rounds.

○ After competing in the Head-to-Head round, the last contestant can claim not only to be the winner, but the winner with a score of 'X' points. Comparing the score with winners of previous games will show who was the winner of the highest scoring game.

THE QUIZMASTER

The key participant in the Weakest Link is the quizmaster. Cutting remarks, rebukes and chastisements are definitely to be encouraged from the quizmaster (although not during the rounds when time is precious) and everybody else just has to grin and bear it because the quizmaster is the boss! If you are lucky enough to be the quizmaster, the comments in the Voting Time sections are really for you to read, so use them in the most entertaining way you can. It's all part of the fun!

As Quizmaster, your key duties are:

○ Ask the questions, starting with the competitor whose first name comes first alphabetically, then moving to his or her left and on through the group.

○ Give the answers and do it quickly. No one wants to be wasting time as the quizmaster bumbles around trying to find the right answer.

○ Keep the time during rounds. Use a stopwatch or a watch or clock with a second hand. If you can't time the rounds, then you have to make sure that each player has the same number of questions per round — make it at least three.

○ Appoint an assistant. It might be useful to get some help from the first weakest link to be voted off. That person can then keep the time for each round or keep track of who's answering questions correctly.

○ After the competitors have revealed their weakest link votes, you should sum up how you thought the contestants did in that round. Make sure you pick up on any of the really silly answers they gave. The Voting Time sections for each round will give you some pointers on cheeky remarks. But do remember it's all for fun! And make sure whoever has been voted the weakest link does the Walk of Shame – once round the room ought to be enough! And don't forget to send them off with the words, 'You are the weakest link ... Goodbye!'

○ Don't be too rude though! Some people might not share your sense of humour and you don't want to start any arguments, do you? Make sure everyone stays calm and that your comments are all part of the fun of playing the Weakest Link.

ROUND ONE
3 MINUTES

So, here you all are at the beginning of the only round where you have a full quota of contestants. This round gives you the most time, the most players and the best chance to show how clever you are. If you're scoring points, this is your chance to get off to a strong start.

But will you?

Are you really up to it?

Who among you is destined to let themselves down? Who among you will hesitate and burble over the answers? Who is a time waster and whose general knowledge is just so shoddy that they shouldn't be taking part at all? Will it be you who has to face the Walk of Shame?

Perhaps each one of you is a genius with a mind and a memory like a NASA computer.

No, I didn't think so.

Are you going to get off to a flying start, or are you going to fall at the first hurdle?

Now is the time to find out.

Let's play the Weakest Link ...

1 How many wives did Henry VIII have?

2 Venus was the Roman Goddess of what?

3 In maths, what is 24 divided by 8?

4 What is the capital of the United States of America?

5 Which 'E' is the TV soap opera featuring Albert Square?

6 In which part of your body would you find the scapula?

7 In food, which country is famous for spaghetti and other types of pasta?

8 Which 'M' married Guy Ritchie in Scotland in December 2000?

9 On which date is St Valentine's Day?

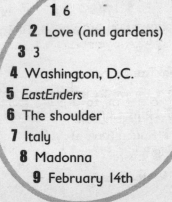

ANSWERS

1 6

2 Love (and gardens)

3 3

4 Washington, D.C.

5 *EastEnders*

6 The shoulder

7 Italy

8 Madonna

9 February 14th

ROUND ONE - 3 MINUTES

1 In which year did the Second World War end?

2 What was the nickname given to nurse Florence Nightingale?

3 What is 8 times 6?

4 What is the name of the longest river in France?

5 What is Bob the Builder's catch phrase?

6 Who wrote the story of 'The Snow Queen' and 'The Ugly Duckling'?

7 Which 'R' is the sport played in the Six Nations Championship?

8 At which time of the year are Simnel Cakes traditionally eaten?

9 True or false – mushrooms are a type of fungi?

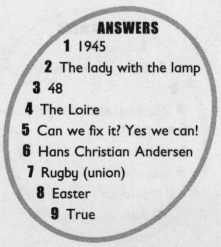

ANSWERS
1 1945
2 The lady with the lamp
3 48
4 The Loire
5 Can we fix it? Yes we can!
6 Hans Christian Andersen
7 Rugby (union)
8 Easter
9 True

ROUND ONE - 3 MINUTES

1 Which 'T' was the long robe worn by men in Ancient Rome?

2 What is half of 30?

3 Who is known as The Naked Chef?

4 In which European country is the city of Amsterdam?

5 Which 'N' is a daily Australian soap opera on BBC 1?

6 Is a tomato a fruit or a vegetable?

7 Which 'A' is the racecourse where the Grand National is held?

8 In literature, which piece of furniture was the gateway to Narnia?

9 In sport, how many events are there in a decathlon?

ANSWERS

1 Toga
2 15
3 Jamie Oliver
4 The Netherlands (Holland)
5 *Neighbours*
6 Fruit
7 Aintree
8 Wardrobe
9 10

ROUND ONE - 3 MINUTES

1 What is the name of the type of boat used by the Vikings?

2 What was the name of Queen Victoria's husband?

3 How many seconds are there in a minute?

4 In television, what skill is Laurence Llewelyn-Bowen most famous for?

5 Where in England would you find the road network known as Spaghetti Junction?

6 In science, what is H_2O better known as?

7 In American Football, what does NFL stand for?

8 Which 'T' is the nickname given to the London Underground?

9 In literature, what is the name of Sherlock Holmes's trusty companion?

ANSWERS

1 Longship

2 Prince Albert

3 60

4 Interior design, (accept decorating, not painting)

5 Birmingham/The Midlands

6 Water

7 National Football League

8 Tube

9 Dr Watson

ROUND ONE - 3 MINUTES

1 How many grams are there in a kilogram?

2 Which 11th Century battle is depicted in the Bayeux Tapestry?

3 Is a cow a vertebrate or an invertebrate?

4 If a window is opaque, can you see through it?

5 Which 19th Century American author wrote *Little Women*?

6 Which 1980's pop duo brought George Michael to fame?

7 True or false – the game of badminton is named after Badminton house, the ancestral home of the Duke of Beaufort in Gloucestershire?

8 Which squirrel is more common in England – red or grey?

9 In which country would you find the Statue of Liberty?

ANSWERS

1 1,000

2 The Battle of Hastings

3 Vertebrate

4 No

5 Louisa May Alcott

6 Wham

7 True

8 Grey

9 America, or USA

1 How many husbands did Queen Elizabeth I have?

2 In maths, what is the decimal equivalent of three-tenths?

3 In geography, what is the largest mountain range in Central Europe?

4 Who wrote *The Jungle Book* and *Just So Stories*?

5 At which annual British tennis championship is it traditional to eat strawberries and cream?

6 In which year was the Great Fire of London?

7 What 'E' does the body make to help digestion that many washing powders also contain?

8 Which word for a pointed human tooth also means 'like a dog'?

9 In which British film, first shown in 2000, did teenager Jamie Bell star as a boy learning to be a ballet dancer?

ANSWERS

1 None

2 0.3

3 The Alps

4 Rudyard Kipling

5 Wimbledon

6 1666

7 Enzymes

8 Canine

9 *Billy Elliot*

ROUND ONE - 3 MINUTES

1 Which American sport were Babe Ruth and Joe Dimaggio famous for?

2 True or false – plants need light to grow?

3 Which 'T' is the river that runs through London?

4 Who is Queen Elizabeth II's eldest son?

5 What is the name given to the 15th Century battles between the houses of Lancaster and York?

6 What colour are the blood cells that carry oxygen around the body?

7 In television, which science-fiction series features agent Dana Scully?

8 In literature, who wrote stories about the Secret Seven?

9 How many days are there in the month of March?

ANSWERS

1 Baseball
2 True
3 The Thames
4 Prince Charles, or The Prince of Wales
5 The Wars of the Roses
6 Red
7 The X-Files
8 Enid Blyton
9 31

ROUND ONE - 3 MINUTES

1 What is the name of the largest desert in the world?

2 Roman Emperors often wore crowns of wreaths made from the leaves of which tree?

3 What 'J' is a place in the body where two bones meet?

4 How many hours does it take for the earth to rotate once on its axis?

5 What is the capital city of Italy?

6 Which boy band did Robbie Williams belong to before he went solo?

7 In the book *Charlie and the Chocolate Factory*, what is the name of the chocolate-factory's eccentric owner?

8 In food, kidney, broad, flageolet and runner are all types of what?

9 In astronomy, which planet orbits closest to the Earth?

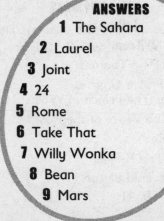

ANSWERS

1 The Sahara

2 Laurel

3 Joint

4 24

5 Rome

6 Take That

7 Willy Wonka

8 Bean

9 Mars

VOTING TIME ...

Well, now you've got the first round out of the way you have to vote off the weakest link. Who did you think displayed a disastrously low level of general knowledge? Which one of you thinks he or she performed worst? Will it be you who is facing the Walk of Shame?

It's time to vote off the weakest link ...

Quizmaster – once the competitors have revealed who they have voted for, remember to give them a hard time. Go back to a contestant who gave a wrong answer and say things like, 'So, [player A], you don't read newspapers, watch TV or listen to the radio? Which M married Guy Ritchie in December 2000? You said it was the Minister. Everyone else realized that Madonna was the answer we were looking for, why didn't you?'

And don't forget to send the weakest link off on the Walk of Shame with the words 'You are the weakest link ... Goodbye!'

ROUND TWO

2 MINUTES 50 SECONDS

Now we move on into Round Two. You have one less player and ten less seconds before another of you bites the dust. Let's play the Weakest Link ...

1 In which country is the Yen the official currency?

2 Near which African city is Table Mountain?

3 Which 1993 Steven Spielberg film was about the return of the Dinosaurs?

4 Which 'Y' is used as a raising agent in bread?

5 Which 'L' was the name given to the armies of Ancient Rome?

6 In which country is the Suez Canal?

7 What colour is associated with the wood ebony?

8 In nature, what 'F' does a tadpole grow into?

9 Who wrote the book *Pride and Prejudice*?

ANSWERS

1 Japan

2 Cape Town

3 *Jurassic Park*

4 Yeast

5 Legion

6 Egypt

7 Black

8 A frog

9 Jane Austen

1 What is the name of the main wall built by the Romans to protect England from the unconquered Scots?

2 Which word did author J. K. Rowling use for people who aren't wizards or witches and don't practise magic?

3 Which yellow flower, regarded as a weed, has a French name meaning 'lion's tooth'?

4 What's the British name for the board game called 'Checkers' in the USA?

5 What 'E' happens when the moon passes between us and the sun?

6 What's the everyday name for the clavicle, the bone around the bottom of your neck?

7 Andre Agassi and Tim Henman are famous players of which sport?

8 A faulty piece of cartilage between bones in the human spine is often called a slipped what?

9 Which 'J' was king of the gods of Ancient Rome?

ANSWERS

1 Hadrian's Wall

2 Muggles

3 Dandelion

4 Draughts

5 Eclipse

6 Collarbone

7 Tennis

8 Disc

9 Jupiter

1 Who was the dictator of Nazi Germany?

2 In Roman numerals, what does X stand for?

3 In television, what is the name of the coffee shop in *Friends*?

4 Named after an animal, on what type of tree do conkers grow?

5 In astronomy, which 'T' is used to look at the stars?

6 What 'N' are the fibres that tell your brain what's happening in the rest of your body?

7 In sport, how many players compete at one time in a game of field hockey?

8 What 'H' is a 3D image visible only when light reflects off it?

9 In fashion, what does a milliner traditionally make?

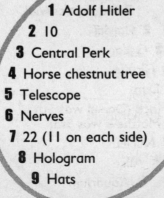

ANSWERS
1 Adolf Hitler
2 10
3 Central Perk
4 Horse chestnut tree
5 Telescope
6 Nerves
7 22 (11 on each side)
8 Hologram
9 Hats

ROUND TWO - 2 MINUTES 50 SECONDS

1 What is the name of the volcano that erupted near the city of Pompeii in AD79?

2 What is the capital city of Wales?

3 Which 'O' is the popular name given to the American Academy of Motion Picture Arts and Sciences Award?

4 In the animal kingdom, what is the tallest animal?

5 Which 'D' is a barrier built across a river or stream?

6 Was Matthew, Daniel, or Jack the most popular name given by parents to baby boys born in Britain in the year 2000?

7 What 'N' is the centre of an atom, or of a plant cell?

8 In the Lewis Carroll books, what was the name of the little girl who had adventures in Wonderland?

9 Which 'A' is a water tank used to house water animals and plants?

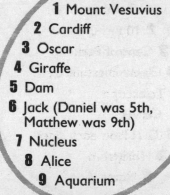

ANSWERS

1 Mount Vesuvius

2 Cardiff

3 Oscar

4 Giraffe

5 Dam

6 Jack (Daniel was 5th, Matthew was 9th)

7 Nucleus

8 Alice

9 Aquarium

1 Which 'W' is a drink also known as Adam's Ale?

2 In which British city would you find the G-Mex Centre?

3 Who is Posh Spice married to?

4 What does the 'e' in e-mail stand for?

5 What do you call a baby horse?

6 Traditionally, what sort of show would you expect to see in a Big Top?

7 What 'G' is the natural sugar your body gets if you eat carbohydrates like potatoes?

8 Which large bird is traditionally said to 'gobble' when it's noisy?

9 What do we call the Palaeolithic Age: the Stone Age, the Bronze Age or the Iron Age?

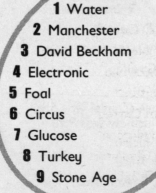

ANSWERS
1 Water
2 Manchester
3 David Beckham
4 Electronic
5 Foal
6 Circus
7 Glucose
8 Turkey
9 Stone Age

1 In which British county is Newquay?

2 How many wheels does a tricycle have?

3 In computers, what does www stand for?

4 In which country did the Aboriginal People invent boomerangs?

5 Which shellfish do the most valuable pearls usually come from?

6 Who starred in the title role of the 2000 film *The Grinch*?

7 What 'H' is the lightest gas, and combines with oxygen to make water?

8 Which trained slaves fought each other in Roman arenas to entertain the crowds?

9 How many degrees are there in a circle?

ANSWERS

1 Cornwall

2 Three

3 World Wide Web

4 Australia

5 Oyster

6 Jim Carrey

7 Hydrogen

8 Gladiators

9 360°

1 What 'P' is the name given to the type of paper used by the Ancient Egyptians?

2 In which American State is the Grand Canyon?

3 What colour is the precious stone ruby?

4 In the animal kingdom, which 'Z' is a black and white striped member of the horse family?

5 Which pop-star mother has a daughter called Lourdes and a son called Rocco?

6 *The Cat Mummy, Vicky Angel* and *The Lottie Project* are titles of books by which popular writer for girls?

7 Which tiny bit of a plant with a membrane around it, has the same name as a monk's room in a monastery?

8 Which plant is the national emblem of Ireland?

9 What is the name given to a female who comes from Paris, France?

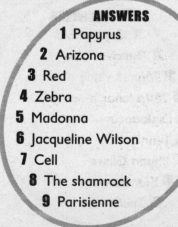

ANSWERS

1 Papyrus

2 Arizona

3 Red

4 Zebra

5 Madonna

6 Jacqueline Wilson

7 Cell

8 The shamrock

9 Parisienne

ROUND TWO - 2 MINUTES 50 SECONDS

1 How old was Lady Jane Grey when she was executed in 1554?

2 What is the longest river in Africa?

3 In nature, bass and turbot are types of what?

4 Approximately how many days does it take the moon to orbit the earth?

5 Which 'D' was one of the longest species of Dinosaur?

6 Love, deuce and advantage are all part of the scoring system for which game?

7 Which members of Steps host the talent show *Steps to the Stars*?

8 In the human body, which 'K' are the organs that filter waste products from the blood?

9 True or false – a diamond is the hardest known natural mineral?

ANSWERS
1 16 years old
2 The river Nile
3 Fish
4 28 (a lunar month)
5 Diplodocus
6 Tennis
7 H and Claire
8 Kidneys
9 True

VOTING TIME ...

Another round down and another performance of which each of you can say you are truly proud – or can you? Are you all pleased with your answers in the last round?

No, I didn't think so.

You think you might do better in the next round? You won't get the chance if you are voted the weakest link. Let's cut out the cloth-heads and banish the bozos.

It's time to vote off the weakest link ...

Quizmaster – after the competitors have voted you are free to discuss their performances. If you've been keeping a record you will know exactly who the weakest link was, and that's not always the competitor who is being voted off. You can say something like, 'So, [Player A], you've voted for [Player B]. You think she should be kicked out of the game – but she wasn't the weakest link, was she? No, statistically you were. No one had more wrong answers than you did ...'

ROUND THREE
2 MINUTES 40 SECONDS

Some of you will be counting yourselves lucky to have survived this far. Still, there's another vote just around the corner. Let's play the Weakest Link ...

1 Which country do the Maori People come from?

2 How many months are there in a trimester?

3 In the human body where is the femur?

4 Which 'G' is the fruit from which most wine is made?

5 Which 'T' was invented by Alexander Graham Bell?

6 What type of tree grows from an acorn?

7 In 1979 who became Britain's first female Prime Minister?

8 Which British TV Personality was originally called Priscilla White?

9 Who is the author of the Harry Potter series of books?

ANSWERS
1 New Zealand
2 Three
3 The leg, or the thigh
4 Grape
5 Telephone
6 Oak
7 Margaret Thatcher
8 Cilla Black
9 J. K. Rowling

1 Which 'E' was the name given to children sent to live in the countryside for safety during the Second World War?

2 Which Olympic sport uses the parallel bars, the asymmetric bars and the beam?

3 Which English playwright wrote *Romeo and Juliet*, *Hamlet* and *Othello*?

4 In 1969, Neil Armstrong became the first man to do what?

5 What happened to the puppet Pinocchio when he told a lie?

6 In music, grand and upright are types of what instrument?

7 In the human body, what are molars and incisors?

8 What is the name given to the sport that uses a bow and arrow?

9 Which Hollywood star married Jennifer Aniston at Malibu, California, in July 2000?

ANSWERS

1 Evacuees

2 Gymnastics

3 William Shakespeare

4 Walk on the moon

5 His nose grew longer

6 Piano

7 Teeth

8 Archery

9 Brad Pitt

1 In which American city is the John F. Kennedy Airport?

2 In the animal kingdom, brown, polar and grizzly are all types of what?

3 What 'G' is the force that holds us down on to the earth's surface?

4 Name the fifth basic sense missing from this list – touch, sight, taste, hearing …?

5 What is the name of Elvis Presley's mansion in Memphis, Tennessee?

6 Which 'unsinkable' ship hit an iceberg and sank in 1912?

7 In karate, what is the colour of the highest belt that can be awarded?

8 What type of food is grown on a paddy field?

9 Which 1930s child actress received an Oscar at the age of six?

ANSWERS

1 New York

2 Bear

3 Gravity

4 Smell

5 Gracelands

6 Titanic

7 Black

8 Rice

9 Shirley Temple

1 What type of bird does a cygnet grow into?

2 In computers, what does IT stand for?

3 Which 'B' is a reading system for those who are blind or partially sighted?

4 In which game does the bull's eye score 50 points?

5 From which animals do we get bacon and ham?

6 In the Enid Blyton books, where do Noddy and Big Ears live?

7 Which British City did the Beatles come from?

8 Which country is also known as the Emerald Isle?

9 In fiction, which little boy attends Hogwarts School?

ANSWERS

1 A swan
2 Information Technology
3 Braille
4 Darts
5 Pigs
6 Toyland
7 Liverpool
8 Ireland
9 Harry Potter

1 Which insect spreads the disease malaria?

2 Which sign of the zodiac is associated with the crab?

3 In which game are woods, irons and putters used to hit the ball?

4 On which TV show did children's TV personality Katy Hill begin her presenting career?

5 Which 'S' was the term used to describe women who were fighting for the right to vote in the early 20th Century?

6 How many months does the average human baby spend in the mother's womb?

7 What is the main ingredient of cheese?

8 Which American pop singer was born Cherilyn Sarkasian?

9 In which country is the Great Barrier Reef?

ANSWERS

1 Mosquito

2 Cancer

3 Golf

4 *Blue Peter*

5 Suffragettes

6 9

7 Milk

8 Cher

9 Australia

1 In nature, what is the largest known mammal?

2 Which 'A' is the name given to a book of maps?

3 In food, is sunflower oil a saturated or unsaturated fat?

4 In *The Muppet Show*, what kind of animal is Kermit?

5 McLaren, Ferrari and Jordan are all teams in which sport?

6 In literature, what was Dr Doolittle's unusual talent?

7 Which former *Neighbours* star had a hit single with Robbie Williams with the song 'Kids'?

8 Which 'M' is the planet nearest to the Sun?

9 In geography, in which country is the Taj Mahal?

ANSWERS
1 The blue whale
2 Atlas
3 Unsaturated
4 A frog
5 Formula One motor racing (accept motor racing)
6 He could talk to animals
7 Kylie Minogue
8 Mercury
9 India

ROUND THREE - 2 MINUTES 40 SECONDS

1 Which insect does silk come from?

2 What is the name, from the Hindi language, given to a one-storey house?

3 On the TV show *Bodger and Badger*, what is Badger's favourite food?

4 Which Spice Girl had a hit with Bryan Adams in 1998?

5 Which Guy plotted to blow up the Houses of Parliament in 1605?

6 Which sport is Tiger Woods famous for?

7 In science which 'M' is a piece of equipment used to magnify tiny objects?

8 Which country does Parmesan cheese come from?

9 Which 'A' describes a severe case of spots on the skin?

ANSWERS
1 Silkworm
2 Bungalow
3 Mashed potato
4 Mel C/Sporty/ Melanie Chisholm
5 Guy Fawkes
6 Golf
7 Microscope
8 Italy
9 Acne

1 Cox's Orange Pippin, Golden Delicious and Granny Smith are all types of which fruit?

2 When VE day was celebrated on May 8th 1945, what did the letters VE stand for?

3 In the original book and film, how many Dalmatians did Cruella de Vil pursue?

4 Which Welsh actress is married to Hollywood superstar Michael Douglas?

5 Front crawl, butterfly and breast stroke are all terms from which sporting activity?

6 Which former *Eastenders* star had a No 1 hit with the record 'Perfect Moment'?

7 What is the source of natural rubber?

8 Which 'A' is the process used to create cartoons?

9 True or false – more than two thirds of the human body is made of water?

ANSWERS

1 Apples

2 Victory in Europe

3 One hundred and one

4 Catherine Zeta Jones

5 Swimming

6 Martine McCutcheon

7 The rubber tree

8 Animation

9 True

VOTING TIME ...

Starting to notice the difference that a few seconds less makes? Or were you just stumbling over answers and clutching at straws? One of you doesn't have to worry about pulling any more answers out of thin air. One of you is about to be dumped. Let's weed out the weakling, fling out the faint-hearted and bin the birdbrain.

It's time to vote off the weakest link ...

Quizmaster – perhaps someone stumbled over their answers in the last round? Think about it as the contestants write down their votes. When they have voted, whether they have voted off the player you have in mind or not, have a go at the time waster. You could say something like, 'Took your time answering in the last round, didn't you [Player A]? I thought you'd forgotten how to speak. What's the matter? Scared you'll get a question wrong?'

Don't forget the catchphrase for the loser – 'You are the weakest link ... Goodbye!'

ROUND FOUR
2 MINUTES 30 SECONDS

Your numbers are dwindling fast. Who will be next to go? This could be your biggest round, or this could be your last round. Let's play the Weakest Link ...

1 Which printed publications can be called tabloid or broadsheets?

2 Which doll did pop group Aqua sing about?

3 Who created Mickey Mouse?

4 In food, which 'Y' is made from fermented milk?

5 In motor racing, what are 'slicks'?

6 If on a menu a fish is described as filleted, what does that mean?

7 In which American city is the Empire State Building?

8 What is the name of the famous stone circle on Salisbury Plain?

9 How many wonders of the ancient world were there?

ANSWERS
1 Newspapers
2 Barbie
3 Walt Disney
4 Yoghurt
5 Tyres (tyres without treads used in dry weather)
6 Bones have been removed
7 New York City
8 Stonehenge
9 7

1 In television, which comedy double act originally hosted the show *Friends Like These*?

2 Which 'M' is the type of drama in which the actors do not speak or make any noise at all?

3 The Boyzone single 'No Matter What' came from which West End musical?

4 In the animal kingdom, does a tiger have spots or stripes?

5 In nature, which mammal squirts a foul-smelling liquid at its enemies when attacked?

6 During Prohibition in 1920's and 30's America, what was made illegal?

7 In the stories by Jill Murphy, how is Mildred Hubble known when she attends Miss Cackle's Academy for Witches?

8 In which English city is Nelson's Column?

9 Which 'B' is a winter sport that can take place on the Cresta Run?

ANSWERS
1 Ant and Dec
2 Mime
3 *Whistle Down the Wind*
4 Stripes
5 The skunk
6 Alcohol
7 The worst witch
8 London
9 Bobsleigh

1 Who painted the Mona Lisa?

2 In which decade did Punk Rockers first become fashionable?

3 Which TV programme followed the lives of a group of people on the Island of Taransay during the year 2000?

4 Which 'H' is the name given to a group of cows?

5 In food, what is caviar?

6 What is the name of the Olympic games held for athletes with disabilities?

7 In humans, which organ does the skull protect?

8 In Science, the three states of matter are solid, liquid and *what*?

9 What sort of a creature was Incitatus, who was made a senator by the mad Roman Emperor Caligula?

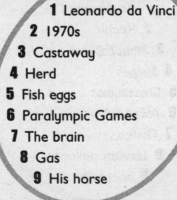

ANSWERS
1 Leonardo da Vinci
2 1970s
3 Castaway
4 Herd
5 Fish eggs
6 Paralympic Games
7 The brain
8 Gas
9 His horse

ROUND FOUR - 2 MINUTES 30 SECONDS

1 In North America, which season is known as Fall?

2 In the animal kingdom, to which family do snakes, lizards, crocodiles and turtles belong?

3 The song 'Supercalifragilisticexpialidocious' comes from which 1964 film about a children's nanny with a magic umbrella?

4 When Stephanie Cook won the Modern Pentathlon at the 2000 Sydney Olympics, she had to compete in how many different sports?

5 Which best-selling series of scary books for children is written by R. L. Stine?

6 In which cartoon film do the Beatles save Pepperland from attack by the Blue Meanies?

7 Cappuccino and espresso are kinds of which drink?

8 Propane gas is used to warm large quantities of air in what sort of transport?

9 In your body, the shoulder and hip joints are known as 'ball and – *what?* joints'

ANSWERS

1 Autumn

2 Reptile

3 *Mary Poppins*

4 5

5 *Goosebumps*

6 *Yellow Submarine*

7 Coffee

8 Hot-air balloons

9 Socket

1 How many days are there in a leap year?

2 Which 'W' is the cowboy hero of *Toy Story* and *Toy Story II*?

3 Blue, minke and humpback are all types of what?

4 In music, Mick Jagger is the lead singer in which rock band?

5 Which fruit is most often used to make marmalade?

6 Which Premier League footballer has an angel tattooed across his shoulders, above the name Brooklyn?

7 The ribcage protects the heart and which other pair of organs in the human body?

8 Iron, copper, zinc and brass — which is the only one that's not an element?

9 According to Roman mythology, the brothers Romulus and Remus were raised by which wild animal?

ANSWERS

1 366
2 Woody
3 Whale
4 The Rolling Stones
5 Orange
6 David Beckham
7 The lungs
8 Brass (it's a mixture of copper and zinc)
9 A wolf

1 In an orchestra, to which section do the violins, cellos and double bass belong?

2 Which actor played agent James Bond in the film *Tomorrow Never Dies*?

3 In nature, what is the original source of cork?

4 Which profession do members of the trade union Equity belong to?

5 Which sport is Chris Eubank famous for?

6 In which classic story by E. Nesbitt, subsequently filmed, do Roberta, Peter and Phyllis help to prevent a train crash while their father is in prison?

7 In a food survey in 2000, children were found to like pasta best of all, but which vegetable did children say they hated most?

8 What 'B' describes material that breaks down and decays harmlessly when thrown away?

9 Mercury, then Venus – then what is the third planet from the sun?

ANSWERS

1 Strings

2 Pierce Brosnan

3 The cork tree (a kind of oak tree)

4 Performing arts/acting

5 Boxing

6 *The Railway Children*

7 Brussels sprouts

8 Bio-degradable

9 Earth

1 In the Green Cross Code, we are told to Stop, Look and … *what?*

2 What is the name of the TV show that gave CBBC presenter Michael Underwood his big break?

3 What is the common name of the tree on which the coconut grows?

4 Which American singer called her chart-topping album by her nickname J-Lo?

5 Which British athlete won the men's triple jump at the 2000 Sydney Olympics?

6 The name Wendy was made popular by which Sir James Matthew Barrie play about the adventures of Wendy Darling and her brothers?

7 In the dessert called Baked Alaska, what is inside the outer covering of meringue and sponge cake?

8 Where in your body is the Achilles tendon, named after a Greek hero?

9 In science, how many straight edges are there on a cube?

ANSWERS

1 Listen

2 *Whatever You Want*

3 Palm tree

4 Jennifer Lopez

5 Jonathan Edwards

6 *Peter Pan* or *The boy who wouldn't grow up*

7 Ice cream

8 Heel

9 12

1 What are members of St John's Ambulance trained in?

2 In the comedy double act, who was Stan Laurel's partner?

3 Which 'P' is a white bear that lives in the Arctic?

4 How many interlocking rings make up the Olympic symbol?

5 The song 'Tomorrow' comes from which musical about a young orphan girl who is looked after by Daddy Warbucks?

6 The book called *Harry Potter et la Coupe Ardente* is a French translation of which English title, the fourth in the series?

7 Which vegetable nickname describes somebody who lounges about watching far too much television?

8 What 'A' was a large Roman arena, like the Colosseum, where wild animals might appear?

9 In science, what 'M' are tiny micro-organisms too small to be seen with the naked eye?

ANSWERS

1 First aid

2 Oliver Hardy

3 Polar

4 5

5 *Annie*

6 *Harry Potter and the Goblet of Fire*

7 Couch potato

8 Amphitheatre

9 Microbes

VOTING TIME ...

There's a certain tension starting to creep in now. Perhaps you're starting to imagine who you might be going Head-to-Head with in Round Nine? Some of you must have highly developed imaginations if you can picture that. Some of you just aren't going to make it. Who's next for the chop? It's time to ditch the deadhead.

It's time to vote off the weakest link.

Quizmaster — come down as hard as you can on anyone who is chatting or larking around. After all, they could be trying to put the others off. Try something like, 'So, [Player A], feeling chatty now, are we? You didn't have quite so much to say when you were asked how many straight edges there are on a cube ...'

Hopefully you will be able to follow up on any troublemakers with the words, 'You are the weakest link ... Goodbye!'

ROUND FIVE
2 MINUTES 20 SECONDS

Feeling confident ... or starting to panic a bit? The clock is ticking. Time is running out for someone else in this round. Will it be you? Let's play the Weakest Link ...

1 In the well-known proverb, what does a stitch in time save?

2 What is Popeye the Sailor Man's favourite food?

3 What type of fruit is grown in a Vineyard?

4 In the performing arts, what is Darcy Bussel famous for?

5 Which 'C' is used to navigate north, south, east and west?

6 To which animal family does the coyote belong?

7 In the Bible, what did God create on the sixth day?

8 What 'A' is a combination of two or more metals?

9 Which metal is associated with a 25th wedding anniversary?

ANSWERS

1 Nine

2 Spinach

3 Grapes

4 Ballet

5 Compass

6 Dog

7 Man (and woman)

8 Alloy, or amalgam

9 Silver

1 What is the national flag of the United Kingdom known as?

2 In nature, which 'C' is a bird that lays its eggs in another bird's nest and leaves them to be hatched by foster parents?

3 Which actor starred in *Grease*, *Saturday Night Fever* and *Pulp Fiction*?

4 Which pop star sang the song 'Circle of Life' from the film *The Lion King*?

5 Great Britain won eleven gold medals in the Sydney Olympics in 2000 – how many were for swimming?

6 Which classic story by Frances Hodgson Burnett, subsequently filmed, tells of Mary Lennox and her friends Colin and Dickon?

7 What 'H' is what a creature like a bear does when it sleeps throughout the winter?

8 What was supplied to the city of Ancient Rome through pipes and channels called Aqueducts?

9 What 'B' is an instrument for measuring air pressure, and helping forecast the weather?

ANSWERS

1 Union Jack, or Union Flag

2 Cuckoo

3 John Travolta

4 Elton John

5 None

6 *The Secret Garden*

7 Hibernate

8 Water

9 Barometer

ROUND FIVE - 2 MINUTES 20 SECONDS

1 What 'C' was a light two-wheeled wagon used by fighting troops in ancient times?

2 If a male horse is called a stallion, what's a female horse called?

3 Which film starring Hugh Grant and Julia Roberts was named after a district of London?

4 'Baby One More Time' and 'Oops, I Did It Again' were big chart hits for which young American singer?

5 What is the name given to an animal that sleeps during the day and is active at night?

6 What 'U' is another word for Hades, where Romans believed souls went after death?

7 What do we call the joint where your leg and foot are connected?

8 What is measured by the little cups that spin round on an instrument called an Anemometer?

9 Is asparagus the name of a fruit, a vegetable, a sauce or a cheese?

ANSWERS

1 Chariot

2 Mare

3 *Notting Hill*

4 Britney Spears

5 Nocturnal

6 Underworld

7 Ankle

8 Wind speed

9 Vegetable

1 Which British Royal residence was badly damaged by fire in 1992?

2 In Arthur Ransome's book *Swallows and Amazons*, were the original swallow and amazons: horses, boats, dogs or islands?

3 In the UK, what does NHS stand for?

4 From which Platform does the Hogwarts Express leave King's Cross Station, in the Harry Potter stories?

5 In *Eastenders*, which business in the square is owned by the ever-absent Mr Papadopolous?

6 In children's TV, which pink, knitted, mouse-like aliens communicated in high-pitched whistles and lived under dustbin lids?

7 In 2001, in which sport did Ellen MacArthur and *Kingfisher* make headlines by finishing second in a long-distance race?

8 In fashion, bell bottoms and flares are types of what?

9 How many players make up a Rugby Union team?

ANSWERS

1 Windsor Castle

2 Boats (the dinghies that the children sailed in)

3 National Health Service

4 9¾

5 The Launderette

6 The Clangers

7 Yachting, or sailing

8 Trousers

9 15

ROUND FIVE - 2 MINUTES 20 SECONDS

1 Could light travel around the earth 3, 7, 11 or 16 times in one second?

2 Eboracum was the Roman name for which historic cathedral city in the north of England?

3 If in a hospital, a patient is taken to the A and E department, also known as Casualty, for what do the letters A and E stand?

4 Which actor sang 'Can We Fix It?', the big Bob the Builder Christmas hit of 2000?

5 Which 'A' was the name given to the separation of races in South Africa?

6 In the nursery rhyme, what did Little Miss Muffet eat when she sat on her tuffet?

7 What type of boats do the RNLI operate?

8 Which 'G' is the heavy make-up used for the Theatre and Circus?

9 Which country uses the leek as a national symbol?

ANSWERS

1 7
2 York
3 Accident & Emergency
4 Neil Morrissey
5 Apartheid
6 Curds and whey
7 Lifeboats (Royal National Lifeboat Institute)
8 Greasepaint
9 Wales

1 What was the title of the 1996 film in which the horrible Mrs & Mrs Wormwood have a gifted daughter, who is taught by Miss Honey?

2 What is the name given to a group of lions?

3 In fashion, from which country does the sari originate?

4 On which date do people in the UK celebrate Halloween?

5 In cockney rhyming slang, what are 'plates of meat'?

6 Which 'S' is a ship that can travel underwater?

7 In film, with which robot character is the English actor Anthony Daniels most commonly associated?

8 In a Christmas animated film, what was the name of the reindeer voiced by comedian Ardal O'Hanlon?

9 What does the 'CD' in CD-ROM stand for?

ANSWERS

1 *Matilda*

2 Pride

3 India

4 October 31st

5 Feet

6 Submarine

7 C-3PO

8 Robbie

9 Compact disc

1 Which island in the Irish Sea is famous for its cats without tails, and for its T. T. motorcycle races?

2 Panathinaikos and Olympiakos are top soccer teams from which country?

3 Which actor starred in the title role of the film *Forrest Gump*?

4 In nature, which animal is sometimes known as the Ship of the Desert?

5 Which country do kangaroos and koalas come from?

6 Why is it so easy to float in the Dead Sea?

7 What was invented by Lazlo Biró in 1944?

8 The French national flag is known as the tricolour – what are the three colours?

9 What does the Thames barrier protect London against?

ANSWERS

1 Isle of Man

2 Greece

3 Tom Hanks

4 Camel

5 Australia

6 Because it is so salty

7 The ball-point pen

8 Red, white and blue

9 Flooding

1 What is the name given to frozen water?

2 In London, at which number Downing Street does the Prime Minister traditionally live?

3 How many metres are there in a kilometre?

4 Wormwood Scrubs, Barlinnie, Pentonville and Dartmoor are all names of what sort of institutions?

5 Which 'C' is a supersonic passenger aircraft?

6 What is Buzz Lightyear's famous catch phrase?

7 What is the children's daily news programme called?

8 In the nursery rhyme, to which English city did Doctor Foster go?

9 Wedgwood and Royal Doulton are both types of what?

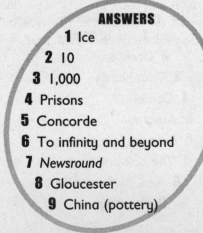

ANSWERS

1 Ice

2 10

3 1,000

4 Prisons

5 Concorde

6 To infinity and beyond

7 *Newsround*

8 Gloucester

9 China (pottery)

VOTING TIME ...

With fewer competitors you should now be enjoying the chance to answer more questions each. Ah, but the time keeps running out, doesn't it? Annoying if you want to show off how smart you are, but a huge relief if you are the one who was struggling to stay afloat in the last round. Well, now it's time to sink or swim. There are no lifelines in this game. Let's weed out the nincompoop and drop the dimwit.

It's time to vote off the weakest link.

Quizmaster — by now you might be growing a little tired of picking on individuals so have a go at the whole lot of them instead. Remember that you can sum up their performance as a whole with, 'And at the end of that round you managed to scrape together a measly total of just three correct answers. The ones left by now are supposed to be the best. You wouldn't think it by that pathetic performance, would you?'

ROUND SIX
2 MINUTES 10 SECONDS

The time is spiraling ever downwards. Two minutes and ten seconds is all you have in this round. For someone it will be the last two minutes and ten seconds of the game. Let's play the Weakest Link ...

1 What is the name of Winnie the Pooh's human owner?

2 In the nursery rhyme, 'Hickory Dickory Dock', which animal ran up the clock?

3 Which part of the body does an optician examine?

4 Mars was the Roman god of what?

5 Which 'W' is the twisted thread in the middle of a candle?

6 What do we usually call the reflective studs in the middle of roads?

7 What is the national flower of England?

8 Copper, tin and aluminium are all types of what sort of element?

9 Fresh oranges are an especially good source of which vitamin?

ANSWERS
1 Christopher Robin
2 A mouse
3 The eyes
4 War
5 Wick
6 Cat's eyes
7 The rose
8 Metal
9 Vitamin C

1 Which 'D' is a national park in Devon, England?

2 In the children's *Mister Men* stories, what colour was Mister Happy?

3 Name the giant radioactive dinosaur that first appeared in a Japanese film in 1954 and has been the subject of many subsequent films and cartoon series?

4 What 'H' is a building used to house an aeroplane?

5 What do Christians call the first thirty-nine books of the Bible, from Genesis to Malachi?

6 Which insect produces honey?

7 What colour is the felt on a UK Snooker table?

8 Which river is crossed near Hull by Britain's longest suspension bridge?

9 What does the 'U' in USA stand for?

ANSWERS
1 Dartmoor
2 Yellow
3 Godzilla
4 Hangar
5 The Old Testament
6 Honey bee (accept bee)
7 Green
8 Humber
9 United

ROUND SIX - 2 MINUTES 10 SECONDS

1 What is the name of the bell in the clock tower at the Houses of Parliament?

2 Which 'C' is a party game where teams have to guess what is being acted out in front of them?

3 Which young singer's first Top Ten album in the UK was called 'Voice of an Angel?

4 Which cartoon character's catchphrase is 'I tawt I taw a puddy tat'?

5 Which 'H' glides across water or land on a bed of air?

6 In history, did the Hundred Years War between England and France last for 98, 100, or 116 years?

7 Who has presented both *The Antiques Roadshow* and *This Is Your Life* on TV?

8 What's the name of the dog in the TV show *The Tweenies*?

9 If you look at a snowflake under a microscope, how many sides does it always have?

ANSWERS

1 Big Ben

2 Charades

3 Charlotte Church

4 Tweety Pie (accept Tweetie)

5 Hovercraft

6 116 years

7 Michael Aspel

8 Doodles

9 6

1 In the year 2000, which female presenter joined Konnie, Simon and Matt on *Blue Peter*?

2 What sort of creature is Sean, the lonely hero of the cartoon film *The First Snow of Winter*?

3 Which national park covers the area of Cumbria containing Windermere?

4 Dendrochronology means finding out the age of *what* by counting the rings inside it?

5 Which long-handled cutting tool used by farmers is found by rearranging the letters of the word CHESTY?

6 Which Scottish actor who used to play James Bond was knighted in 2000?

7 Which breed of dog chases a stuffed hare in races around a stadium?

8 When a computer monitor is called a VDU, what do those letters mean?

9 Which major river does the M25 motorway cross twice as it circles London?

ANSWERS

1 Liz (Liz Barker)

2 Duckling (accept duck)

3 The Lake District

4 A tree (when the trunk is cut through)

5 Scythe

6 Sir Sean Connery

7 Greyhound

8 Visual Display Unit

9 The Thames

1 The name of which beautiful Greek god was picked for the mission that first took men to the Moon?

2 In children's toys, what is the name of the toy figure that springs out of a box when it is opened?

3 In which year did the first Superman comic strip appear — 1938 or 1945?

4 The E-Type, the S-Type and the X-Type are models of which British-built motor car?

5 Who traditionally makes a speech that is televised at 3 p.m. each Christmas Day?

6 In which central London square, famous for its lions, do people traditionally get together to celebrate New Year?

7 Which young actor played the overlooked Kevin McCallister in the 1990 film comedy *Home Alone*?

8 In which district of London was the Millennium Dome built?

9 In the 1995 film *Toy Story*, what is the name of the astronaut who refuses to believe he really is a toy?

ANSWERS

1 Apollo

2 Jack in the box

3 1938

4 Jaguar

5 The Queen (accept the reigning monarch)

6 Trafalgar Square

7 Macaulay Culkin

8 Greenwich

9 Buzz Lightyear

1 Which famous person's 100th birthday was widely celebrated on August 4th 2000?

2 Which character does a Whoop-de-Dooper bounce in the Hundred Acre Wood, in a Disney cartoon first seen in 2000?

3 Which is the nearest capital city to the EuroDisney theme park?

4 How are the brothers Paul and Barry Elliot better known on their long-running series of comedy TV shows for children?

5 By what name do most people know Henry Charles Albert David of Wales?

6 What is the surname of the top American chat-show host whose first name is Oprah?

7 A traveller who is nicknamed a Kiwi comes from which faraway Commonwealth country?

8 What sort of institutions are Papworth, Great Ormond Street, and Barts (St Bartholomew's)?

9 What did the British designer Trevor Baylis invent in 1993 that works by clockwork?

ANSWERS

1 The Queen Mother (accept the Queen Mum)

2 Tigger, in *The Tigger Movie*

3 Paris

4 The Chuckle Brothers

5 Harry or Prince Harry

6 Winfrey

7 New Zealand

8 Hospitals

9 Radio

1 According to the proverb, what do many hands make?

2 Which professor is the Pokémon expert who is Gary's grandfather?

3 At which time of the year do people celebrate Hogmanay, especially in Scotland?

4 'What's up, Doc?' is the catchphrase of which cartoon rabbit?

5 Which bear with a bandage over his eye is the mascot of the Children in Need charity appeal?

6 When it's winter in Britain, it's summer in Australia, so in which month do Australians celebrate Christmas?

7 Was Chloe, Lucy or Rebecca the favourite name chosen by parents for baby girls born in Britain in the year 2000?

8 Which name that means 'darling' in French is the first name of Mrs Tony Blair?

9 Which word can mean a high-value playing card, a hole in one at golf, and a real expert?

ANSWERS

1 Light work

2 Professor Oak

3 New Year (accept 31st December)

4 Bugs Bunny

5 Pudsey (bear)

6 December

7 Chloe – Lucy was 10th and Rebecca was 12th

8 Cherie

9 Ace

1 Shane Lynch from Boyzone has sisters in which band?

2 Which word can mean both a part of a plant that takes in oxygen and a page of a book?

3 For what does the first 'D' stand for in the Video Disc system known for short as DVD?

4 What is the name of the border collie who joined the cast of *Blue Peter* in 2001?

5 On a boat, starboard is right – what is left?

6 In the nursery rhyme, why did Jack and Jill go up the hill?

7 Which superhero went under the everyday name of Clark Kent?

8 In which TV series do wishes come true when a certain part of a coin is rubbed?

9 In French language, what is the usual English translation of *au revoir*?

ANSWERS

1 B*witched
2 Leaf
3 Digital
4 Meg
5 Port
6 To fetch a pail of water
7 Superman
8 *The Queen's Nose*
9 Goodbye

VOTING TIME ...

By now your numbers have dwindled to quite an intimate little group, but the pressure is building. Are you the one who is struggling to search out those answers that you know are lurking there in the back of your memory? Will you be the one the others choose to loose? It's time to lighten the load, bump off the blunderer and delete the ditherer.

It's time to vote off the weakest link.

Quizmaster – if the game started with the optimum number of nine contestants, then you will be going in to Round Seven with just three. Hopefully you now have some help from the weakest links to do the timekeeping. That means that you can concentrate even more on your dialogue. Make them squirm!

ROUND SEVEN

2 MINUTES

Now things are really getting serious. There's nowhere to hide. Which of you can take all that in your stride and march on into the final stages with confidence and which of you is about to slip up? Let's play the Weakest Link …

1 Which fruit is said to have led Isaac Newton to discover gravity?

2 What is the French word for 'yes'?

3 Which 'O' is the large cartoon friend of Asterix the Gaul?

4 *Simba's Pride* is the sequel to which Disney film set in Africa?

5 In the nursery rhyme, who had lost her sheep?

6 Is an aardvark: a mammal, an insect, a bird or a reptile?

7 What's the name of the charity for which people collect on Red Nose Day?

8 In which French city is the Eiffel Tower?

9 What colour is associated with the disease jaundice?

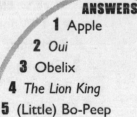

ANSWERS
1 Apple
2 *Oui*
3 Obelix
4 *The Lion King*
5 (Little) Bo-Peep
6 Mammal
7 Comic Relief
8 Paris
9 Yellow

1 Which little yellow bird is Snoopy's friend in the Peanuts cartoon strip?

2 What 'M' was the technique used by the Romans for decorating floors with tiny pieces of tile and glass?

3 In the olden days, what 'C' were soldiers who fought on horseback, though today they probably ride in tanks?

4 Which word is used for a child in a classroom and for a part of the human eye?

5 In the 1939 film *The Wizard of Oz*, what did the lion ask the wizard to give him?

6 In literature, which author wrote the children's book *George's Marvellous Medicine*?

7 In which hit film of 1999 do an American family adopt a mouse, much to the annoyance of their cat, Snowbell?

8 What is a male pig called?

9 How many people were there in the 1970's pop group Abba?

ANSWERS

1 Woodstock

2 Mosaic

3 Cavalry

4 Pupil

5 Courage

6 Roald Dahl

7 *Stuart Little*

8 Boar

9 4

1 Dead Metal, Sir Killalot, Shunt and Matilda make regular appearances on which technological TV show?

2 What is the name of Queen Elizabeth II's official London residence?

3 In the United Kingdom what is the telephone number for the emergency services?

4 In Europe, which Country is most associated with the tulip?

5 What is the name of Santa Claus's red-nosed reindeer?

6 The flag of which country is known as Old Glory or the Stars and Stripes?

7 What colour are the beak and legs of a healthy Flamingo bird?

8 Which TV presenter set up the charity Childline in 1986?

9 In the children's TV animation, what is the name of the postman who owns Jess – a black and white cat?

ANSWERS

1 *Robot Wars*

2 Buckingham Palace

3 999

4 Holland, or Netherlands

5 Rudolf

6 United States of America

7 Pink

8 Esther Rantzen

9 Pat

1 Mrs Tiggywinkle and Peter Rabbit are characters from which author's stories?

2 In the Bible, what was the name of the sea that Moses crossed to reach the Promised Land?

3 Which word is used for a paper hankie and for the material out of which body cells are made?

4 True or false – the male seahorse carries and hatches the female's eggs?

5 What name is given to the Friday before Easter Day?

6 Which 'H' is a prickly creature that rolls into a ball when scared?

7 In cartoons what is the name of Huey, Dewey and Louie's uncle?

8 How many wheels does a unicycle have?

9 Which 'O' is the world's largest living bird?

ANSWERS
1 Beatrix Potter
2 Red Sea
3 Tissue
4 True
5 Good Friday
6 Hedgehog
7 Donald Duck
8 One
9 Ostrich

1 What colour is the poppy that is sold to mark Remembrance Sunday?

2 What is the nickname given to the underground railway network in Paris, France?

3 In which London park is London Zoo?

4 What 'S' is the acid that falls from the sky, in very weak form, in what we call 'acid rain'?

5 What did the ancient Romans store underground in long caves called catacombs?

6 Which Monty Python star has also travelled around the world in eighty days, and from Pole to Pole to make documentaries?

7 Dick King-Smith's book *The Sheep-Pig*, about a pig that learns to herd sheep, was given what new title when it was filmed in 1995?

8 In which event do competitors zigzag between poles, either in canoes or on skis?

9 What type of toy is named after American president Theodore Roosevelt?

ANSWERS

1 Red

2 Metro

3 Regent's Park

4 Sulphuric

5 Bodies of the dead

6 Michael Palin

7 *Babe*

8 Slalom

9 Teddy bear

1 In which game does the winner shout 'House!'

2 In English law, how many people make up a jury: 10, 12 or 15?

3 In 1998, who was the first singer to leave The Spice Girls?

4 In the 2001 Disney cartoon *The Emperor's New Groove*, Emperor Kuzco is magically turned into which South American animal?

5 Which surname is shared by boxer Lennox, newsreader Martyn, and singer Shaznay of All Saints?

6 On Boxing Day 2000, a Radio 4 broadcast recording of *Harry Potter and the Philosophers' Stone* was read by which well-known actor?

7 Midsummer Night, the shortest of the year, falls in which month in Britain?

8 What 'A' was an ancient counting-frame device, still used today to help solve mathematical problems?

9 In nature, is an acacia a butterfly, a flower, a tree or a semi-precious stone?

ANSWERS

1 Bingo, or Lotto

2 12

3 Geri Halliwell (Ginger Spice)

4 Llama

5 Lewis

6 Stephen Fry

7 June

8 Abacus

9 Tree

ROUND SEVEN - 2 MINUTES

1 In technology, which type of aircraft takes off vertically, using a single rotating blade?

2 Steve Davis and Stephen Hendry are former world champions at which game?

3 What is a herbicide used to kill?

4 Geographically, are St Albans and Hatfield in: Hampshire, Hertfordshire or Herefordshire?

5 What do archaeologists call the picture-language used by Ancient Egyptians?

6 Who wrote the music for the musicals *Evita* and *The Phantom of the Opera*?

7 In film, what is the name given to the pair of hinged boards smacked together during filming to help synchronize sound and picture?

8 Complete the title of the following traditional children's party game, 'Pin the Tail on the … *What?*'

9 How many tentacles does an octopus have?

ANSWERS

1 Helicopter

2 Snooker

3 Plants, especially weeds

4 Hertfordshire

5 Hieroglyphics

6 Andrew Lloyd Webber

7 Clapperboard

8 Donkey

9 9

1 Which magazine campaigns against homelessness and first hit the streets in 1991?

2 How many arms does a typical starfish have?

3 Which 'G' was a London theatre that William Shakespeare both acted in and wrote for?

4 Which former pop star of Spandau Ballet moved on to play Steve Owen in *EastEnders*?

5 Which invention of 1907 helped ease washday blues?

6 What is James Bond's secret agent number?

7 Which 'J' is married to Mr Punch?

8 In the fairy tale, how many dwarves did Snow White befriend?

9 In the TV series *The Muppet Show*, what instrument did Animal usually play?

ANSWERS

1 *The Big Issue*

2 5

3 The Globe

4 Martin Kemp

5 (Electric) washing machine

6 007

7 Judy

8 7

9 Drums

VOTING TIME ...

If you started with the optimum nine contestants, then there are now just three left.

Look at your two friends. Are they really your friends? Two of you will go on to the Head-to-Head round ... and those two are about to get rid of their last piece of baggage. Who has been enjoying a free ride for too long?

It's time to vote off the weakest link.

Quizmaster – now you really have to keep your wits about you. The final two competitors are the smartest cookies in the jar and this is their last chance to show off before they go Head-to-Head. If you are keeping score, they will want to answer as many questions as they can so that whoever is the ultimate winner finishes with a high point score. You're going to have be very slick in giving the answers and keeping track of the score.

You only have one more chance to use it after this so make the most of your catchphrase, 'You are the weakest link ... Goodbye!'

ROUND EIGHT
1 MINUTE 50 SECONDS

So, it's the last round and you're still here. Are you really up to it, or have you managed to bluff your way right up to the end of the game? This is where we find out. Let's play the Weakest Link ...

1 Which part of your body might be called the pate or the cranium?

2 Which everyday luxury comes from the cacao plant?

3 In food, molasses is also known as what?

4 Matadors and flamenco dancers are associated with which country?

5 What 'H' is another name for a mouth organ?

6 What sort of creatures are a hobby and a merlin?

7 Which historic battle took place in Sussex on October 14th, 1066?

8 On which coast of France is Monaco, north, south, east or west?

9 The Pacific islands of Hawaii are a state of which country?

ANSWERS
1 Head
2 Chocolate, or cocoa
3 Treacle, or sugar
4 Spain
5 Harmonica
6 Falcons, or birds
7 The Battle of Hastings
8 South
9 The USA

1 What's the usual name for the sneezing and snuffling caused by an allergy to pollen?

2 In underwater diving, what is Self-Contained Underwater Breathing Apparatus better known as?

3 Which organ acts as a rhythmic pump, forcing blood around the body?

4 In Egyptian Mythology, the sun god Horus had the head of what type of bird?

5 Since 1997, Sarah Michelle Gellar has played which vampire-slayer on TV?

6 Which cartoon dog is friends with Fred, Daphne, Velma and Shaggy, and has a nephew called Scrappy?

7 The Battle of the Little Bighorn was fought in which country?

8 What is the first name of Homer's wife in the TV cartoon, *The Simpsons*?

9 What is the name given to the popular children's toy, devised by Richard James in the 1940s, made up of several feet of flat wire coiled into circles?

ANSWERS

1 Hay fever

2 Scuba

3 Heart

4 Hawk or falcon

5 Buffy (Summers)

6 Scooby-Doo

7 USA, America

8 Marge

9 Slinky

1 Which indoor sport do the American Harlem Globetrotters play?

2 In 2000, which pop singer was given a Ferrari by her DJ friend, Chris Evans, even though she couldn't drive?

3 Which sport is featured in the stage musical *The Beautiful Game*, by Andrew Lloyd Webber and Ben Elton?

4 In the Disney film *The Hunchback of Notre Dame*, who is the beautiful gipsy girl with a pet goat called Djali?

5 Which evergreen plant produces white berries and is hung up as a Christmas decoration?

6 In the book *Moby Dick*, what sort of creature was Moby Dick himself?

7 When a shower comes down as little pellets of ice instead of water, what do we call it?

8 What do we call the pit vipers that make loud buzzing warnings by vibrating their tails?

9 In the British countryside, which is larger, an adult rabbit or an adult hare?

ANSWERS

1 Basketball

2 Billie Piper

3 Football, or soccer

4 Esmeralda

5 Mistletoe

6 Great white whale (accept whale)

7 Hail, or hailstones

8 Rattlesnakes

9 Hare

1 In the TV sitcom, Sharon and Tracy are 'Birds of a ...' What?

2 Which feline cartoon character appeared on the titles of the Inspector Clouseau films?

3 Which 'H' are official stamps on silver, gold and platinum to help prevent fraud?

4 Hammerhead, tiger and great white are varieties of which creature?

5 Which popular golden rodent pets are all descended from the same family found in Syria?

6 In music, which instrument has up to 47 vertical strings set into a triangular wooden frame?

7 Mombasa is a port in which African country, famous for its safari holidays?

8 Which regular children's TV show is named after the flag flown by a ship leaving harbour?

9 The champion American golfer Eldrick Woods is always known by what animal nickname?

ANSWERS

1 Feather

2 The Pink Panther

3 Hallmarks

4 Shark

5 Hamsters

6 Harp

7 Kenya

8 *Blue Peter*

9 Tiger (Woods)

1 What liquid is produced by female whales and other mammals to feed their young?

2 Is a mink a member of the cat, the rabbit or the weasel family?

3 Which name is used for hawks, for jump-jet fighters and for cross-country runners?

4 The earth has only one natural satellite – what is it called?

5 Which colourful arch in the sky is caused by light shining through distant raindrops?

6 Which fruit is dried to make a raisin?

7 Which rodent with large ears and scaly tail proverbially scuttles away from a sinking ship?

8 Does the 1976 film *Bugsy Malone* feature a cast of animals or a cast of children?

9 What was the first name of the new baby born in the TV comedy *The Royle Family* in 2000?

ANSWERS

1 Milk
2 Weasel
3 Harriers
4 The moon
5 Rainbow
6 A grape
7 Rat
8 Children
9 David

1 Which reptile, related to the crocodile, lives in the Everglade swamps of Florida?

2 In TV, which broadcaster has a teletext service called Ceefax?

3 Which ancient Chinese method treats patients by sticking needles into the human body?

4 In TV, can you name two of the children in the Tweenies?

5 Which film about a ship hitting an iceberg was the first movie for nearly 40 years to win 11 Oscars?

6 In the series of *Free Willy* films, what sort of creature is Willy?

7 Of which city did Dick Whittington become Lord Mayor?

8 What is Paddington Bear's favourite sandwich filling?

9 According to the song, how many colours are there in a rainbow?

ANSWERS

1 Alligator

2 BBC (BBC1 or BBC2)

3 Acupuncture

4 Jake, Fizz, Bella or Milo

5 *Titanic*

6 Whale – accept orca or killer whale

7 London

8 Marmalade

9 7

1 Which singer won Best Video and Best Single at the 2001 Brits for 'Rock DJ'?

2 A fan of which sport would look for information in a book known as Wisden?

3 In which film about a flying car did Sally Ann Howes play Truly Scrumptious?

4 What's the name of the tortoise who appears on TV with Bill and Ben, the Flowerpot Men?

5 In nature, what 'A' is another name for the snake we call a viper?

6 Allosaurs, Brontosaurs and Stegosaurs were all kinds of which ancient creatures?

7 According to the nursery rhyme, 'Sing a Song of Sixpence', how many blackbirds were baked in a pie?

8 What have you lost if you are suffering from Amnesia?

9 What 'U' is a technique of using sound waves medically to examine an unborn baby?

ANSWERS

1 Robbie Williams
2 Cricket
3 *Chitty Chitty Bang Bang*
4 Slowcoach
5 Adder
6 Dinosaurs
7 Four and twenty, 24, or two dozen
8 Your memory
9 Ultrasound

1 In the TV sitcom, *The Adams Family*, what was the name of the butler?

2 Animals like anteaters are called 'edentate', meaning that unlike people, they have no what?

3 Which TV cartoon cat was frequently chased by Officer Dibble and was loosely based on Sergeant Bilko?

4 Which word for an insect's feeler is also a device for receiving radio signals?

5 In the 1994 film, what was the name of the Pet Detective played by Jim Carrey?

6 What 'M' was a huge hairy prehistoric elephant, now extinct?

7 In the *Captain Pugwash* TV cartoons, what is the name of the pirate ship captained by Cut-Throat Jake?

8 Ariel, Eric, Flounder and Sir Grimsby are characters in which Disney cartoon film containing the song 'Under The Sea'?

9 Which word can mean 'weapons' or 'human limbs'?

ANSWERS

1 Lurch

2 Teeth – think of the word dentures

3 Top Cat (accept Boss Cat)

4 Antenna

5 Ace Ventura

6 Mammoth, or Mastodon

7 *The Flying Dustman*

8 *The Little Mermaid*

9 Arms

ROUND NINE
HEAD-TO-HEAD

This is it! You've had your chance to impress everyone. You've shrugged off the opposition until it's all down to just two of you. Let's see who's up to the challenge!

You will now each have to answer up to five questions each in turn. The one who gets the most right, wins. If you each answer the same number of questions correctly, then the game goes into 'Sudden Death'. Slip up now and you will be the last player of the game to hear the dreaded words:

'You are the weakest link ... Goodbye!'

1 What does a Philatelist collect?

2 Agoraphobia is a fear of what?

3 What is measured in watts, amps and volts?

4 In science, a chronograph is used to measure what accurately?

5 The River Amazon flows into which ocean?

6 Anthracite is a hard, shiny form of what fossil fuel?

7 In folklore, which king of Ancient Britain was the son of Uther Pendragon?

8 Which massive space telescope was launched into orbit in 1990?

9 In Greek mythology, Hera was the queen of the gods – who was the king?

10 In sport, how many events are there in an Olympic heptathlon?

ANSWERS

1 Stamps
2 Open spaces
3 Electricity
4 Time
5 Atlantic
6 Coal
7 King Arthur
8 Hubble space telescope
9 Zeus
10 7

1 The abbreviation MHz, often found on radios, stands for which word?

2 In astronomy, a star that is cool, faint and small is called a 'Red ... ' what?

3 Which white-haired scientist was famous for his Theory of Relativity?

4 What sort of a monster was Cerberus, which in Greek myth guarded the entrance to the Underworld?

5 In 1998, Geri Halliwell became a Goodwill Ambassador for which organization?

6 In 1927, *The Jazz Singer* was the first film to have what added?

7 Which branch of mathematics involves adding, subtracting, multiplying and dividing numbers?

8 Which London landmark is guarded by Beefeaters?

9 On which island in the UK did Queen Victoria die?

10 Sir Edmund Hillary and Tenzing Norgay were the first people to reach the summit of which mountain on May 29 1953?

ANSWERS

1 Megahertz

2 Red Dwarf

3 Albert Einstein

4 Three-headed dog

5 The United Nations

6 Sound, or a sound track

7 Arithmetic

8 Tower of London

9 The Isle of Wight

10 Everest

1 Does India, China or the USA make the most films every year?

2 How many thousands are there in one million?

3 In the Greek legend, how many eyes did a member of the Cyclops race have?

4 What sort of creature is Bilbo Baggins, in Tolkien's book?

5 Jitterbug, Paso Doble and Mazurka are three different kinds of what activity?

6 Who designed St Paul's Cathedral?

7 What is the capital city of Denmark?

8 What is the square root of 144?

9 What was the surname of the brothers who built the first successful aeroplane?

10 In which British country is the Forth Road Bridge?

ANSWERS

1 India
2 1,000
3 1
4 A Hobbit
5 Dance (do not accept music)
6 Sir Christopher Wren
7 Copenhagen
8 12
9 Wright
10 Scotland

1 The tomb of which ancient Egyptian boy king was discovered by Howard Carter in 1922?

2 What was the name of the world's first postage stamp?

3 In Jonathan Swift's famous story, which country did Gulliver visit where the people were all less than one-tenth his size?

4 How many empty squares are there on a chessboard at the start of a standard game of chess?

5 Which mythical king was said to have been born at Tintagel in Cornwall?

6 What are the names of Prince Andrew's daughters?

7 In which year did the Berlin Wall come down?

8 Of which country is Beijing the capital?

9 Rubella is one of the three diseases that the MMR inoculation protects against; what are the other two?

10 Sushi and teriyaki are foods that come originally from which country?

ANSWERS

1 Tutankhamun
2 Penny Black
3 Lilliput
4 32
5 King Arthur
6 Beatrice and Eugenie
7 1989
8 China
9 Measles & mumps
10 Japan

1 What colour are the leather-covered benches on which Members of Parliament sit in the House of Commons?

2 In which large church was Queen Elizabeth II both married and crowned?

3 What is the name given to our galaxy?

4 What is the name of the code communication system that uses flags?

5 Crotchet, minim, quaver and semi-quaver – which of these musical notes lasts for the longest number of beats?

6 Which thoroughfare gives its name to the business centre of New York City?

7 Where was Yuri Gagarin the first man to go?

8 Which American city, nicknamed The Windy City, was gangster Al Capone's home in the 1920s?

9 In history, though Marie Antoinette was born in Vienna, she became queen of which country?

10 The Lynx and the Ocelot are members of which family of animals?

ANSWERS

1 Green
2 Westminster Abbey
3 The Milky Way
4 Semaphore
5 Minim
6 Wall Street
7 Space
8 Chicago
9 France
10 Cat

1 In astrology, which constellation represents the scales of justice?

2 Which metal has often been called quicksilver because of its colour and the way it flows?

3 What sort of creature are a cardinal and a cassowary?

4 An antitoxin is used to fight the harmful effects of what on the human body?

5 In which continent might you see creatures called an aardwolf, an aardvark and an aasvogel?

6 Which language did the people of Ancient Rome speak?

7 In science, decibels are a measure of what?

8 In humans, what passes through the Aorta?

9 Which Victorian author wrote *Far from the Madding Crowd* and *Tess of the D'Urbervilles*?

10 When a leveret grows up, what does it become?

ANSWERS

1 Libra
2 Mercury
3 Birds
4 A toxin, or poison
5 Africa (South Africa)
6 Latin
7 Sound, or noise
8 Blood
9 Thomas Hardy
10 A hare

1 At room temperature, is chlorine a solid, a liquid or a gas?

2 Which planet named after a Roman god is the largest in our solar system?

3 In science, HOW MANY straight edges are there on a triangular prism – 3, 6 or 9?

4 Which city, capital of Zimbabwe, used to be called Salisbury?

5 Who is the patron saint of Scotland?

6 What is the national sport of Canada?

7 What does YMCA stand for?

8 Which author wrote *Treasure Island*?

9 In which decade was the style of dancing known as the Charleston most fashionable?

10 How many sides does a hexagon have?

ANSWERS

1 Gas
2 Jupiter
3 9
4 Harare
5 St Andrew
6 Ice hockey
7 Young Men's Christian Association
8 Robert Louis Stevenson
9 1920s
10 6

1 Which secondary school has educated both Prince William and Prince Harry?

2 In which English town was William Shakespeare born?

3 In which famous bicycle race does the overall leader wear a yellow jersey?

4 Who was the founder of the Scout movement?

5 Who is the leader of the Roman Catholic Church?

6 Is the country of Libya in north, south, east or west Africa?

7 In human biology, what is the more common name for the epidermis and dermis?

8 Which household item was invented by John Logie Baird?

9 Cirrus, cumulonimbus and cumulus are all types of what?

10 In which country would you find the ancient pyramid of Cheops?

ANSWERS

1 Eton College
2 Stratford-upon-Avon
3 Tour de France
4 Robert Baden-Powell
5 The Pope
6 North
7 Skin
8 The television set
9 Cloud
10 Egypt

SUDDEN DEATH

Unbelievably, the last two contestants have proved to be as good as each other. Or are they just as bad as each other? There can be no draws in this game though. So, are you going to be the winner or the loser, the strongest link or the weakest link?

This is where we find out. This is Sudden Death.

The rules are simple. The questions come in pairs. [player A] if you get your question right then [player B] will have to answer correctly or they will lose. [player A] if you get your question wrong and [player B] answers correctly, they will win.

Ultimately, one of you is about to hear those words of doom:

'You are the weakest link ... Goodbye!'

1 Is a locust a type of beetle, grasshopper, worm or flying ant?

2 What do we call the daily record of events on board a ship or aircraft?

3 The city of Los Angeles is found on the coast of which American state?

4 In business, what does the abbreviation LTD stand for?

5 When a camera is called an SLR, what do the letters stand for?

6 What type of food from Australia is a macadamia?

7 Which American pop star had hits with 'Vogue' and 'Ray of Light'?

8 Malaysia and Singapore are part of which continent?

9 What kind of bird is a mallard?

10 Is a chinchilla a kind of dog, goat, rodent or opossum?

ANSWERS
1 Grasshopper
2 Log
3 California
4 Limited
5 Single Lens Reflex
6 Nut
7 Madonna
8 Asia
9 Duck
10 Rodent

1 What 'C' is a word for a homing pigeon that bears a message, and for a sick animal that may infect another?

2 Russians call their spacemen cosmonauts, but what are American spacemen called?

3 What 'C' is the natural stimulant in tea and coffee that makes the heart beat faster?

4 Which word for a video camera is a combination of the words 'recorder' and 'camera'?

5 Non-identical twins are usually known by which name, literally meaning 'brotherly'?

6 In the BBC children's TV series, what are hunted by Mrs Croker, and her revolting side-kick De-Sniff?

7 Which famous 1977 science-fiction film starring Alec Guinness did George Lucas direct?

8 The first spacecraft to land men on the moon was named after which bird?

9 What 'C' is a flexible length of links, or an old measurement of 22 yards?

10 Leatherback is the largest variety of which creature that lays its eggs in sand on the sea shore?

ANSWERS

1 Currier

2 Astronauts

3 Caffeine

4 Camcorder

5 Fraternal

6 Ghosts, in *Ghosthunter*

7 *Star Wars*

8 Eagle

9 Chain

10 Turtle

1 On which parts of your body are you most likely to suffer from chilblains in cold weather?

2 In which long-running TV comedy series did Richard Wilson play the grouchy Victor Meldrew?

3 What do bird-watchers call the seasonal movement of birds to distant breeding or feeding grounds?

4 A megalith is a massive monument built from what material?

5 Victor, Hugo and Laverne are three gargoyles in which Disney cartoon film set in Paris?

6 In Greek mythology, Midas turned whatever he touched into which material?

7 What 'M' is a type of severe or splitting headache?

8 In which hit film of 2000, described as 'The Great Escape, with chickens', is Mel Gibson the voice of Rocky the Rooster?

9 In geography, in which American state are Miami and Miami Beach?

10 Loch Ness is the deepest loch in which country?

ANSWERS

1 Fingers and toes

2 *One Foot in the Grave*

3 Migration

4 Stone

5 *The Hunchback of Notre Dame*

6 Gold

7 Migraine

8 *Chicken Run*

9 Florida

10 Scotland

1 In geography, what's the English name for what Scots call a 'loch'?

2 Near which English city does the Clifton Suspension Bridge cross the River Avon?

3 Is latex a kind of cotton, rubber, plastic or silk?

4 If you were suffering from laryngitis, which bit of you would be sore?

5 What was the title of the children's TV drama about a boy called Jamie Custer who wants to be a professional comedian?

6 What do we call the hot liquid rock that pours out of volcanoes?

7 In the TV puppet show, what is the name of Fireman Sam's red engine, whose number is J999?

8 When tanned animal skin is used to make shoes and clothes, what do we call it?

9 Is a leech, which feeds on blood, a kind of: worm, bat, centipede or beetle?

10 The singer John Lennon was a member of which world-famous pop group?

ANSWERS

1 Luke

2 Bristol

3 Rubber

4 Throat, larynx, or windpipe

5 *Custer's Last Stand-up*

6 Lava, or magma

7 Jupiter

8 Leather

9 Worm

10 The Beatles

SUDDEN DEATH

1 Grapefruit, lime, lemon, kiwi fruit and orange – which one is NOT a citrus fruit?

2 Is a cockatiel a kind of parrot, hawk, seagull, or chicken?

3 Inside what silky sheath do many insects live immediately before they hatch out?

4 Which delicate fabric, used as decoration on dresses, was made in places like Nottingham, Honiton and Chantilly?

5 In the classic cartoon film *Bambi*, what sort of black and white animal was Flower?

6 In which TV puppet series does Lady Penelope Creighton-Ward drive in a pink Rolls-Royce, with the numberplate FAB.1?

7 In a TV series like *L.A. Law* or a film like *L.A. Confidential*, for what does L.A. stand?

8 In sport, what device is found at the end of a lacrosse stick?

9 In the nursery rhyme, which beetle is advised to 'Fly away home' because her home is on fire?

10 In which county in England's north-west are Blackpool and Morecambe?

ANSWERS

1 Kiwi fruit
2 Parrot
3 Cocoon
4 Lace
5 Skunk
6 *Thunderbirds*
7 Los Angeles
8 A small net
9 Ladybird
10 Lancashire